D1510675

Simple Pleasures©
for Special Seniors

Life in The
US MILITARY

Images for Reflection & Reminiscence©
For Veterans with Memory Loss

Due to Alzheimer's Disease, Other Dementias and Causes

Life in The

US MILITARY

Simple Pleasures for Special Seniors© Life in The US MILITARY©
Images for Reflection & Reminiscence©
All Rights Reserved.
©2011 Dan Koffman

Simple Pleasures Books
260 Saylor Road
Camano Island, WA 98282
360-387-3024
www.SimplePleasuresBooks.com -&- www.LifeInTheUSMILITARY.com

No part of this publication may be reproduced, stored in a retrieval system,
or transmitted, in any form or by any means, electronic, mechanical, photocopying,
recording or otherwise, without the written permission of the author.

First published by Dog Ear Publishing
4010 W. 86th Street, Ste H
Indianapolis, IN 46268
www.dogearpublishing.net

ISBN: 978-145750-274-3

This book is printed on acid-free paper.

Printed in the United States of America

Foreword

"Those of you who are familiar with World War II, Korean, and Vietnam Era Veterans know that the war was the defining experience of their lives. They were young and idealistic when they entered into the war and their service there shaped who they became for the rest of their lives. This is true even for those Veterans who have started to experience memory loss. The warrior may be on furlough but he is not gone.

The good news is that this deep-rooted self-identity provides family members, caregivers, and healthcare workers a direct line into the heart and soul of the aging warrior who is suffering from memory loss. Good communication is especially critical for maintaining social ties with family members and to ensure that the Veteran has input into his or her healthcare decisions. When memory fades, so does normal communication. Veterans with memory loss become frustrated and confused. Often they suffer in silence, not knowing how to reach out to others. As a result, family members become exasperated and resentful, thinking that they have been deliberately excluded. When communication breaks down, all parties become isolated. No one has control and no one can take control. Everyone suffers.

All parties become the victims of poor communication brought on by memory loss of a loved one. Watching someone you love suffer from memory loss is dreadful. Friends and family members suffer alongside their affected loved ones. And often they, too, suffer in silence.

This silence must be broken. For communication to be improved, it becomes a priority for us to clarify thoughts and feelings about how to communicate and about what to communicate. Tools must be created to break down the communication barriers that arose as a result of that memory loss.

To begin this process, think about what you miss most. Chances are that some of the memories you have of your loved one involve wartime stories. Do you want to see, even one more time, the jaunty sailor who swept your mother off her feet, or the proud soldier who bought his family a home with proceeds from the GI Bill, or the dedicated WAC who opened her own small business to support a family that she and her now deceased husband had started in the optimism of the post war boom? Would you want to have Aladdin's Lamp to give you one more chance to hear that off-key rendition of 'Don't Sit Under the Apple Tree'? Do you miss that special story and do you want to hear it again?

For those of you who answered yes, then Aladdin's Lamp has granted your wish in the form of this book. Dan Koffman's *Life in The US MILITARY* is a simple book. It offers simple solutions to the communication quandary. And it is simply wonderful.

Mr. Koffman has handed us a true gift of time disguised as a book. With his book we can reverse the silence that has started to descend into our interactions with our Veterans as a result of their memory losses. This book does not create new memories; instead it unlocks the old ones. It contains simple pictures that can evoke deep memories and emotions. Pictures of boots, buzz cuts, and barracks represent simple ideas but evoke powerful emotions. They give us an opportunity to engage in conversations, ask questions, and to reminisce. Be prepared to sit back and marvel at the sound of a long-absent voice chuckling over pup tents, backpacks and 'borrowed' jeeps; rejoice in the return of that wicked gleam in the eye; and rue the day you once were foolish enough to have said 'If I have to listen to that story one more time I will scream'. Who knew how we would come to miss those stories. And now there is a possibility of having some of that back again, perhaps not with the full power of the past, but certainly with the gentle healing power of an echo, sent back to remind us of what once was there.

Although we didn't know it until they were gone, these stories and experiences defined our parents, siblings, spouses, relatives and friends. It gave them context and it reminded them, and now us, that these Veterans were just men and women who were trying to get by and just do their jobs. They were ordinary people caught up in extraordinary events. The Veterans survived those times and were able to make sense of them through their memories and their stories. Who knew that we, their family and friends, would have some hope of hearing pieces of those memories again through the gift of simple pictures, pictures that we recognize as iconic but that we had not realized were actually part of our souls as well?

By addressing the Veteran who lives deep in the core that defines our loved one, this book offers us an opportunity to glimpse that past life, those defining moments, and those wonderful memories. We now have a key to better communication to the life of one we feared was lost forever.

Dan Koffman's *Life in The US MILITARY* reminds us that, while old soldiers never die, they can fade away. You hold in your hands a gift that will delay that fading of your Veteran."

Nina Tumosa, Professor of Internal Medicine/Geriatrics at Saint Louis University,
Co-Director of the Gateway Geriatric Education Center
Editor of Aging Successfully - Saint Louis, Missouri

Dedication

I dedicate this book to my dad and mom, Jack and Dorothy Koffman, and to the many family members, friends and professionals who are loving caregivers to US Military Veterans who have Alzheimer's disease and other forms of dementia.

My dad entered the Army in 1944 at the age of 39. He and my mom closed their three successful retail locations and my dad put his unique business skills to work as an educator for U.S. soldiers returning home after suffering battlefield disabilities ranging from lost limbs to blindness. Stationed at Dibble General Hospital in Menlo Park, California, my dad wrote training manuals specifically designed to assist these disabled veterans identify and establish new businesses they could successfully operate after the war with the assistance offered by the GI Bill. My mom was a civilian employee of the Army and worked along side my dad, no doubt assisting in the creation of these unique training manuals. In his later years, my dad often spoke with pride about having been able to contribute positively to the lives of these disabled veterans.

Dad was diagnosed with dementia in the 1980s and passed away in the 1990s. Mom was his primary caregiver and she passed away just six months later. I am all too familiar with the pain, frustration and sadness visited upon a family in these circumstances. That is why I created this book. *And this book works!*

In the world of Alzheimer's and dementia, moments of connection and sharing are often few and far between. The images in this Simple Pleasures book are simple and powerful and can spark quiet reflection and deeply moving shared experiences. They can create opportunities for communication between family members of all ages and their Special Veteran . . . opportunities for precious shared moments that will be treasured always. There is simply nothing more important.

I know that my folks would agree.

As an addition to this dedication, I want to acknowledge my incredible wife, Sandy. You are my inspiration and you illuminate my life with your warmth and compassion. I love you for eternity.

Jack and Dorothy Koffman, 1945

How To Use This Book

The bold images in this unique book are designed to encourage communication between Veterans with moderate to advanced memory loss and their family members of all ages as well as their caregivers. "Let the book do the work" and, most importantly, be patient, be a good listener and follow these simple guidelines for best results:

CHOOSE THE BEST TIME & PLACE:
○ Be in tune with the Special Veteran's most positive, awake, alert and most lucid patterns as response will be greatly enhanced.

○ Perform Simple Pleasures book activity in a calm and positive environment.

USE THESE SPOKEN CUES TO DRAW OUT THEIR PARTICIPATION:
○ "What do you see?"

○ "What thoughts does this picture give you?"

○ "What feelings does this picture give you?"

○ "Tell me a story about a 'jeep' (or whatever the picture is)?"

○ Listen and wait to see what happens.

○ Be very patient . . . linger on the pages . . . look for facial responses: smiles, thoughtfulness . . . audible responses . . . laughter, or any sounds or comments.

○ Empathize . . . wear their shoes . . . this is for them.

PERSONALIZABLE PAGES AT THE END:
○ Note that at the end of the book, a couple of pages have been left blank for you to add other specific images that may be of special meaning to your Special Veteran.

"Enjoy every precious moment of joyous connection . . . and treasure every day!"
Dan Koffman

Please let us know how it goes. We very much want to hear your comments and especially any and all comments from your Special Veteran.

For more info or questions, contact Dan Koffman at 360-387-3024 or dan@koffman.net

This Book Belongs to:

_____

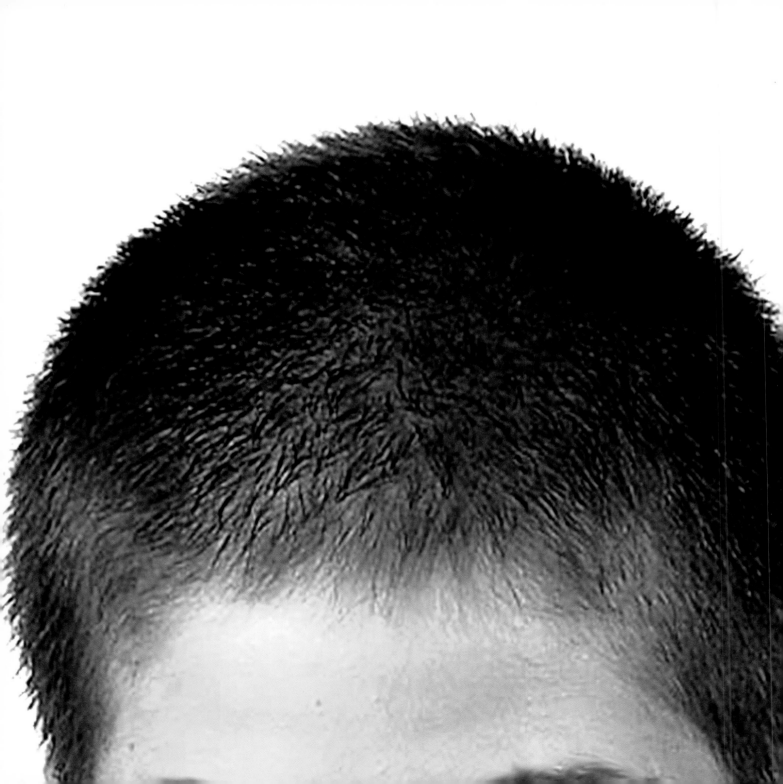

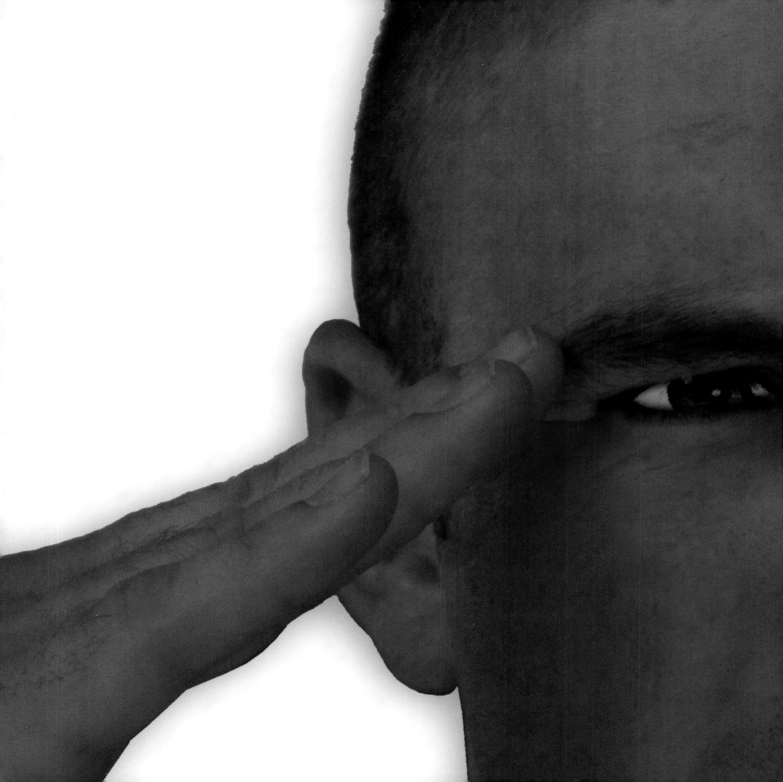

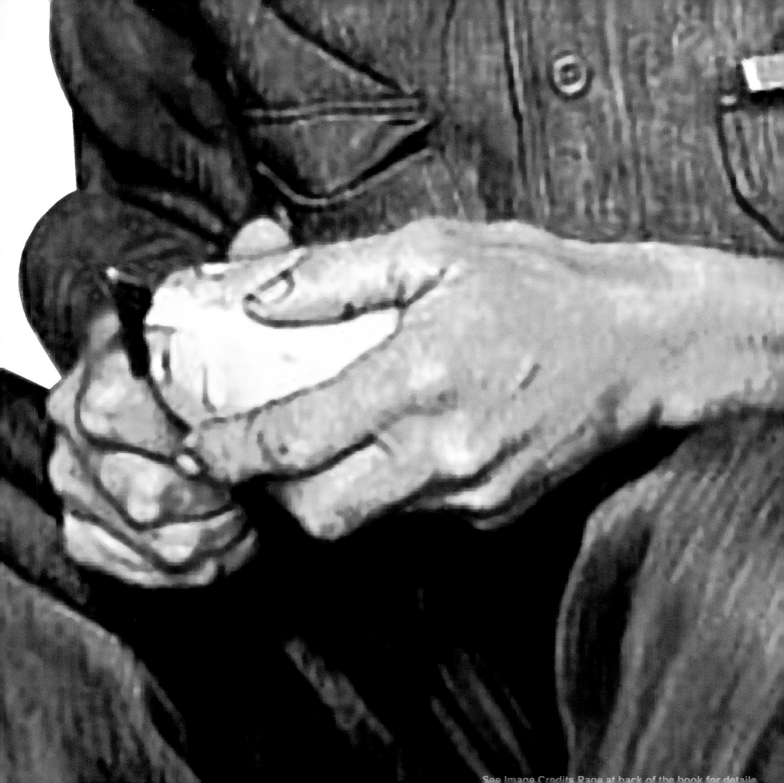

See Image Credits Page at back of the book for details.

Photo by 3rd Signal Company, 3rd Infantry Division. Courtesy dogfacesoldiers.org

PERSONALIZE THIS PAGE WITH A SPECIFIC IMAGE THAT HAS PARTICULAR MEANING TO YOUR LOVED ONE

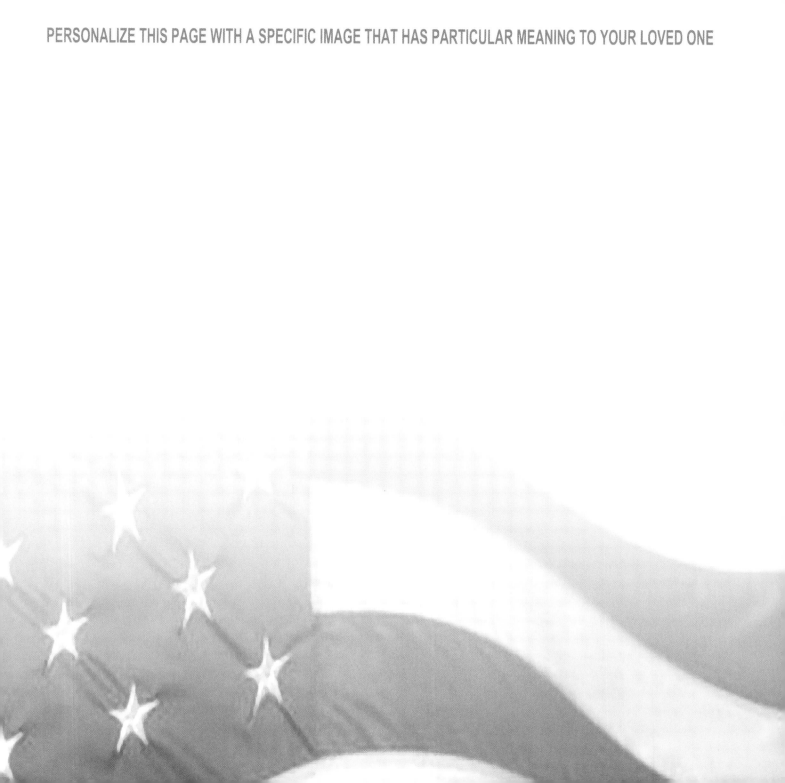

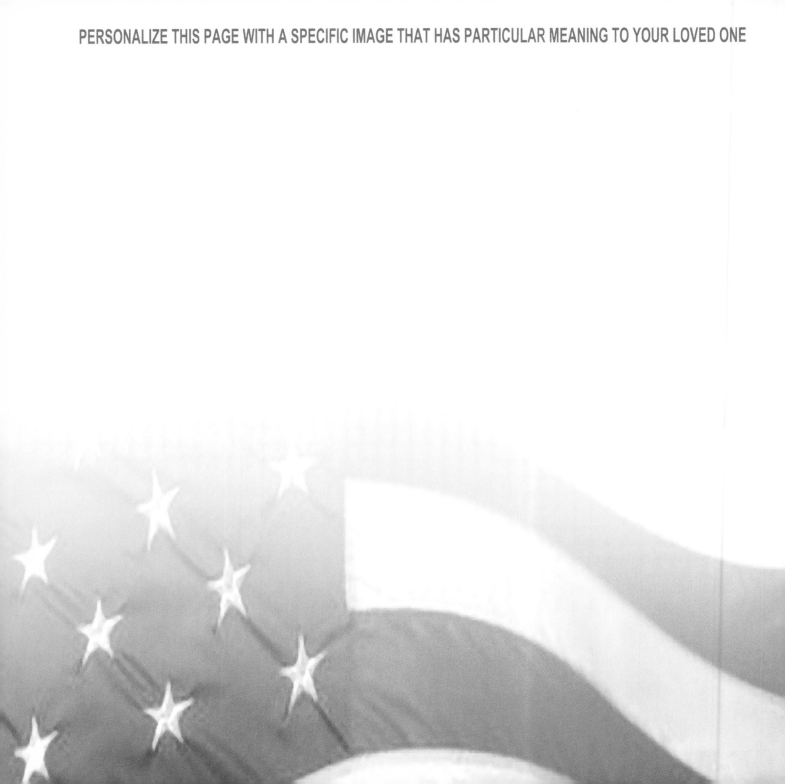

PERSONALIZE THIS PAGE WITH A SPECIFIC IMAGE THAT HAS PARTICULAR MEANING TO YOUR LOVED ONE

PERSONALIZE THIS PAGE WITH A SPECIFIC IMAGE THAT HAS PARTICULAR MEANING TO YOUR LOVED ONE

Acknowledgements and Image Credits

"THANKSGIVING: Mother and Son Peeling Potatoes"
(Cropped Image of Soldier's Hands) Used by Permission:
Painting by Norman Rockwell
Courtesy of the Norman Rockwell Family Agency

"BOB HOPE - USO Entertaining the Troops"
Photo Used by Permission:
3rd Signal Company, 3rd Infantry Division.
Courtesy of dogfacesoldiers.org

Simple Pleasures for Special Seniors© Other Titles Available

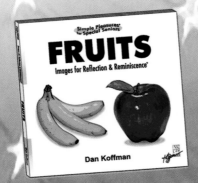

. . . And Many More to Follow! www.SimplePleasuresforSpecialSeniors.com

We would love to hear from you about your loved one's reactions to the "Life in The US MILITARY" book.
Follow us on Facebook or Twitter or visit www.LifeInTheUSMILITARY.com to tell us your story.

About The Author

Dan Koffman is a creative communicator. Throughout his more than 45 year career, he has communicated as a graphic, commercial and fine artist, designer and marketer of consumer products, community activist and now as the creator of the Simple Pleasures for Special Seniors© series of books designed specifically for people with memory loss.

Born in 1950 in Los Angeles, California, Koffman focused first on industrial design and architecture, winning a Gold Medal for his building designs at the California State Fair in 1966 and serving as a draftsman on the Mariner Mars Project – all before completing high school.

From 1970 to 1990 he applied his bold and colorful artistic style to over 1000 internationally marketed consumer products for his company, Bibi Products, Incorporated.

In 1990 he established Bottomline Communications, an international advertising agency in Monterey, California, working with corporations worldwide (including Honeywell, Diners Club, Libbey Glass, Toshiba and financial institutions), injecting unexpected, humorous twists into otherwise traditional marketing, merchandising and advertising campaigns.

Giving back to the community both locally and internationally has always been an integral part of Koffman's life. To that end, he designed the Flag of Peace and Freedom, painted for peace with an African elephant, launched the Golden Rule Activist project and has spearheaded various other community programs.

The experience of witnessing the progression of his father's dementia and the toll it extracted on his mother who was the primary caregiver and his entire family registered deeply in his heart and mind. Koffman says, "I wanted to do something that would have a positive effect on other families going through this same difficult experience. The Simple Pleasures for Special Seniors© books are the realization of that goal."

Dan and his wife Sandy live on Camano Island in Washington State.

You can read more about Dan Koffman by visiting his websites:

www.SimplePleasuresforSpecialSeniors.com
Details on upcoming titles. Hardcover versions of
current titles are available directly from the website.

www.ArtWithaSmile.com
Koffman's art that celebrates people's passions.

www.PeaceFlag.org
Details on the Flag of Peace and Freedom Project.

www.TheManAndTheElephant.com
The story of his artistic collaborations with Lisa the African
elephant and their goal of focusing attention on man's
relationship and responsibility to animals and to our planet.

www.GoldenRuleActivist.com
His project to draw attention to the universal message of the Golden Rule.